A VISIT TO THE
HOSPITAL

Written by FRANCINE CHASE
Pictures by KEN ROSSI
Prepared Under the Supervision of
LESTER L. COLEMAN, M.D.
With an Introduction by Flanders Dunbar, M.D.

WONDER BOOKS · NEW YORK
A Division of GROSSET & DUNLAP, Inc.

INTRODUCTION

By Flanders Dunbar, M. D., Med. Sc. D., Ph. D.
Editor-in-Chief, Emeritus, American Psychosomatic Society

Each year, thousands of children all over America enter hospitals for operations. Usually, it is for the removal of tonsils and adenoids, but whether it is for a hernia, eye or any other operation, even an emergency one, the emotional preparation of the child is most important.

Children can be frightened and shocked by contacts with new and unexplained places. Many children are familiar with parks, theaters, libraries and churches in their own towns. But fewer children know about hospitals — and, as with most things about which little is known, hospitals may appear as mysterious and frightening places.

The children who are not frightened are often the ones who have been told ahead of time everything that is about to happen to them. Too frequently, when children are not told why they are going to a hospital, and why they are being separated from their parents, they may become fearful, suspicious and resentful.

Many of these children stay angry and for years, sometimes, remain resentful toward those who took them to the hospital. These children may carry needless scars of unpleasant hospital experiences into adolescence and adulthood.

At times, parents who have themselves been frightened by surgery, have difficulty in explaining a hospital and an operation to their own children.

That is why Dr. Lester L. Coleman had this book prepared. Parents and children who read it will find it easier to understand and talk about the reasons for operations, hospitalization, anesthesia and the brief period away from home.

Physicians, too, will be glad to have the suggestions given to help make a visit to the hospital a growth experience. A little time in thoughtful preparation can add immeasurably to the immediate and future security and happiness of the children who are about to make their first visit to the hospital.

First Library Edition Printed in 1974.

Library of Congress Catalog Card Number 73-16843
ISBN: 0-448-13183-8 (Library Edition)
1974 PRINTING

STEVIE was sick in bed with a cold. "Why do I have so many colds?" he asked his mommy.

"I'm sorry, dear," Mommy answered. "Maybe it's your tonsils that are giving you so many colds."

"What are tonsils?" Stevie asked.

"Tonsils are two little things in the back of our throats," Mommy said. "When children are little, their tonsils help to keep them well, but when they grow older—like you, Stevie —tonsils very often cause colds and sore throats. Then they're not needed any more, so the doctor takes them out."

"Is it time for my tonsils to come out?" Stevie asked.

"Well," Mommy said, "we'll have to see the doctor first."

When Stevie was well again, he and his mother took a bus ride to the doctor's office.

"Hi, Stevie," the doctor called out. "Your mother tells me that you've been having lots of sore throats and colds lately. Let me take a look at your throat."

Stevie opened his mouth wide.

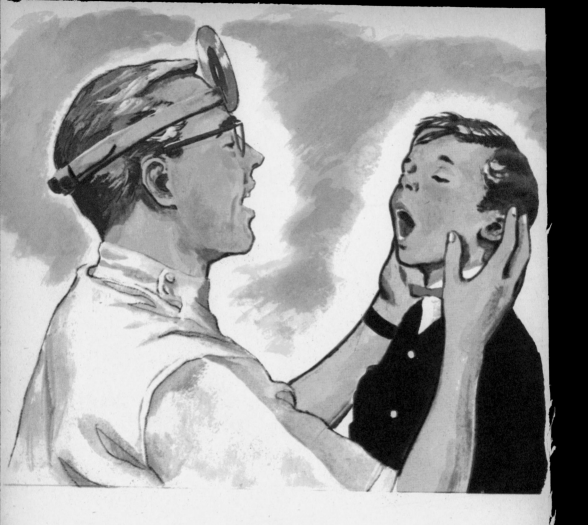

"Well," said the doctor. "Just as I thought. It's those tonsils. We'd better take them out."

The doctor and Mommy decided that next Tuesday would be a good day to go to the hospital to take out the tonsils. Stevie wasn't sure he liked this. But the doctor explained everything so nicely and he was so friendly, that it made Stevie feel better.

"How long will I have to stay at the hospital?" asked Stevie.

"Only one day and one night," the doctor answered.

When they got home Mommy told Stevie all about the tonsil operation. She told him that she and Daddy would be with him at the hospital. Stevie knew everything that was going to happen, so there was nothing to worry about.

When Tuesday morning came, Stevie woke bright and early. He packed his own suitcase. Into it he put his bathrobe, slippers and favorite sleep toy. It wasn't really a toy. It was just an old piece of baby blanket that he loved to sleep with.

Mommy said, "You shouldn't have breakfast today because the doctor says that if you don't eat just before you have your tonsils out, you'll feel better afterward."

Stevie was too excited to care about breakfast. He wasn't even hungry.

In a little while, they were at the hospital. Inside, there were many ladies dressed in white uniforms and white caps.

"These ladies are nurses," said Stevie's mommy. "They help the doctors and they also help to make the patients more comfortable."

"Good morning, Stevie," said one of the nurses.

Then they all went up to Stevie's hospital room. His daddy showed him that the hospital bed had handles attached to it. By turning the handles, the ends of the bed could be raised or lowered.

"This is fun," he giggled, as his daddy made the bed go up and down with Stevie in it.

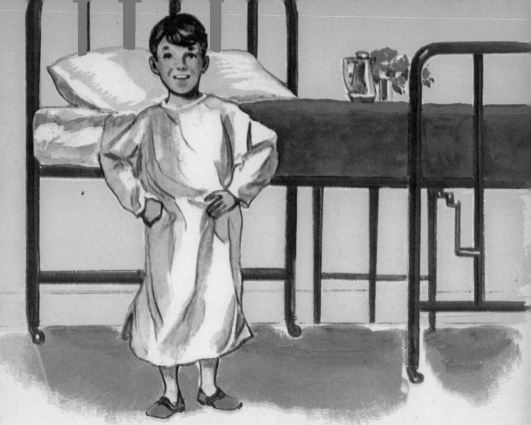

Later, a nurse gave Mommy a little white jacket, and said, "This is for Stevie to put on. It looks like the one his doctor will wear in the operating room." Daddy helped him put on the jacket. "Well, hello, Dr. Stevie," he said.

"Will I be in the operating room long?" Stevie asked.

"No, it takes only a little while," Mommy answered, "about as long as it takes us to walk to the playground and back to the house again."

"Will it hurt?"

"No," Mommy said. "Remember, I told you that you won't feel anything—because you'll be fast asleep."

"Why do I have to go to sleep?" he asked his mother.

"When children have a tonsil operation," Mommy explained again, "the doctor helps them go to sleep so that they won't feel any pain. In fact, you'll be so fast asleep, you won't even know that he is taking out your tonsils."

"How does he do that?" Stevie asked.

"The doctor will let you blow into something that looks like a balloon. It has a funny smell—something like my nail polish," said Mommy. "After you take a few big breaths, you'll fall fast asleep. Then the doctor will take your tonsils out. When you wake up, your throat will feel sore, but it will get better and better every day. And when you get home you may have all the ice cream and soda pop you like, because that will make your throat feel good."

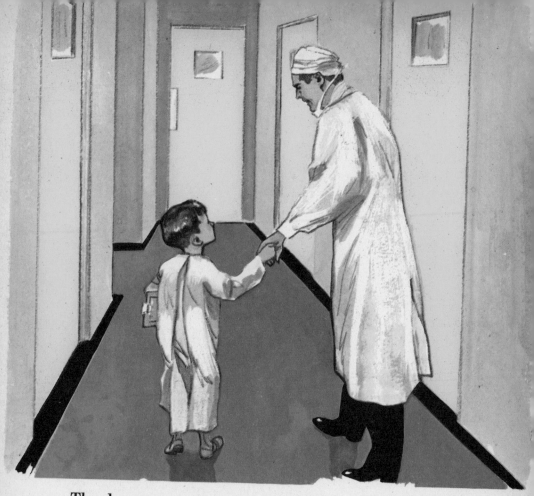

The doctor came into the room. He was wearing a white jacket, just like Stevie's. They talked for a minute, then off they went together, Stevie and the doctor, to the operating room. Going down the hall, they had fun pretending that Stevie was the doctor's assistant. Other doctors and nurses were waiting in the operating room to help Stevie's doctor. They were wearing white, too, and little masks that covered their noses and mouths. "Hello, Stevie," said one of the nurses.

"We all have to wear masks," the doctor said, "because if any of us has a cold, you won't catch it when our noses and mouths are covered."

The doctor asked Stevie to lie down so that he could take out his tonsils.

"Now, just pretend that you're going to blow up this balloon," the doctor said. "Take a good, deep breath, blow into the balloon, and count to ten."

The balloon smelled funny, just as Mommy had said it would. But Stevie took a good, deep breath and began to count. "One . . . two . . . three . . . four . . . five . . . six . . ." and before he got to seven, he was asleep.

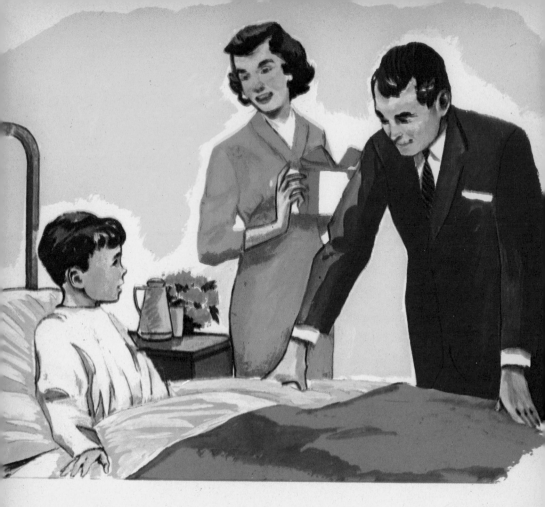

The doctor waited until Stevie was fast asleep. Then he quickly took out the tonsils. It didn't hurt Stevie at all because the doctor let Stevie stay asleep until the tonsil operation was all over.

When Stevie woke up, he was already back in his own hospital room with his mommy and daddy.

"My throat hurts," said Stevie.

"Yes, son," said his daddy. "We told you that your throat would be sore after the operation. But it's going to feel better and better every day. Then you won't have so many sore throats any more. That's why we're so happy that your tonsils are out. The doctor says you were a wonderful patient."

Later, the nurse brought him ice cream and cool soda pop. It did make his throat feel better.

That night, Stevie had a good sleep in the hospital. A little light was left on in his room so that he could see the push button near his bed.

"If you need anything during the night," said the nurse, "all you have to do is push the button. That will ring a bell outside and I'll come right in."

But Stevie didn't use it at all because he slept so well. He was so sound asleep that he didn't even hear the nurse come in to see if he was comfortable.

Early the next morning, when Stevie woke up, he saw his mother and father in the room.

"It's time to go home, dear," Mommy said.

She helped him get dressed. Then they said good-by to the nurses.

"Good-by, good-by!" waved Stevie.

"Good-by!" said the nurses, waving back. "You were a fine little patient, Stevie."

On the way home, Stevie had a big, wide grin on his face. "Daddy," he said very proudly, "when I grow up, guess what I'm going to be?"

"What will you be?" Daddy asked, smiling.

"Well," answered Stevie, "I'm going to be a doctor!"